Also by Reimena Yee

The World in Deeper Inspection
The Carpet Merchant of Konstantiniyya

Reimena Yee

Séance Tea Party

RH
GRAPHIC

Séance Tea Party was conceptualized in a Moleskine notebook, sketched and penciled using Procreate on an iPad Pro, then colored and finished in Photoshop. It was lettered in the author's hand.

Cover art, text, and interior illustrations copyright © 2020 by Reimena Yee

All rights reserved. Published in the United States by RH Graphic, an imprint of Random House Children's Books, a division of Penguin Random House LLC, New York.

RH Graphic with the book design is a trademark of Penguin Random House LLC.

Visit us on the Web! RHKidsGraphic.com • @RHKidsGraphic

Educators and librarians, for a variety of teaching tools, visit us at RHTeachersLibrarians.com

Library of Congress Cataloging-in-Publication Data
Names: Yee, Reimena, author, artist.
Title: Séance tea party / Reimena Yee.
Description: First edition. | New York : RH Graphic, [2020] | Audience: Ages 8–12. | Audience: Grades 4–6. | Summary: After watching her circle of friends seemingly fade away, Lora is determined to still have fun on her own, so when a tea party leads Lora to discovering Alexa, the ghost that haunts her house, they soon become best friends.
Identifiers: LCCN 2019043693 | ISBN 978-1-9848-9415-1 (paperback) | ISBN 978-0-593-12532-8 (hardcover) | ISBN 978-1-9848-9416-8 (library binding) | ISBN 978-1-9848-9417-5 (ebook)
Subjects: LCSH: Graphic novels. | CYAC: Graphic novels. | Ghosts—Fiction. | Best friends—Fiction.
Classification: LCC PZ7.7.Y44 Se 2020 | DDC 741.5/973—dc23

Designed by Patrick Crotty

MANUFACTURED IN CHINA
10 9 8 7 6 5 4 3 2 1
First Edition

A comic on every bookshelf.

To every child—and young
adult—who is afraid of
growing up.

When I was ten, I read fairy tales in secret and would have been ashamed if
I had been found doing so. Now that I am fifty, I read them openly. When I
became a man, I put away childish things, including the fear of childishness
and the desire to be very grown up.

—C. S. Lewis

2

Sup, Lora!

Race ya to class!

Bobby, wait!

See ya later.

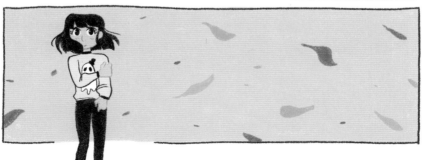

10

Carol
happy birthday Lo!

Nasrul
it's 2day already?

(15) new messages
06:30
Fri, Oct 30

Bobby
haha
Oct 28th
Can I borrow your notes?
Yep.

Where are you?

12

MYSTERIES

Bobby
Fast lyfe

Last online:
Yesterday,
9:13 pm

Sigh

Hmm, wowee.

The world is so strange and fancy.

Don't you agree, Lucky?

Whatcha reading?

Ooh, spooky!

Phantasm

Ghosts!

Do you think they are real?

I heard my school was built on top of a grave site...

But that's, like, every school in the country.

Why do ghosts like being in school so much?

BLEH!

If I were a ghost, you know where I'd haunt?

Disneyland.

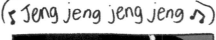

Eep!

No, no! Don't go away!

I'm a friend.

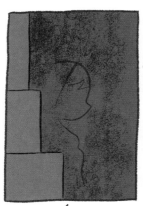

There you go!

Oh wow! Are you really a ghost?

Discovery TV is gonna get a kick outta this!

What's your name?

Alexa.

Hey! I'm Lora Xi!

How long have you stayed here?

I don't know. A long time, maybe?

WOW! I had no idea our house is haunted. Do you usually show up like this?

No... I mean, I'm a ghost.

People run away from ghosts...

Oh, okay.

Do you have any ghost friends?

No. Just me.

You must be lonely, then...

17:51
Oct 30

That's the afterlife.

That's life too.

HEY! Let's be friends!

Oh?

Sure, if you want.

Really?

I've never heard of anyone being actual friends with a ghost before.

What do you think that would be like?

(Well—)

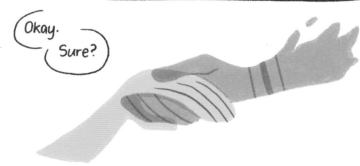

Me and my imaginary friend — we used to do everything together.

We climbed trees, played house, and actually...

We used to dance like this too.

Like we were two princesses, waltzing in a ball —

Oof!

Oh no!

I'm sorry! I forgot to make myself corporeal.

Haha. No worries. It's cool.

Can I touch you now?

plap

Chapter 2: Halloween

Here's our little witch!

Happy Halloween.

Any spooky plans with Bobby today?

Nope! He hasn't had time lately.

I'm hanging out with Alexa instead.

Oh, who's she?

The ghost who lives in our house.

We're best friends now.

Cool, cool.

Eh, ah girl, don't you think you're too old to play like this?

You're 12, right?

Shouldn't girls your age be into... I dunno —

Boy bands and fashion?

BLEH!

WHAT lah, you! Why are you so in a rush for her to grow up?!

PIAK

oi!

Lora, I remember you had an imaginary friend when you were small. Both of you had so much fun!

And the way you used to talk about them...

It was almost like they were real.

Okay, wait, humor me. Do you think this friend might actually be a... ghost, haunting us?

snorts No.

I don't think so. Do you?

Who knows?

There's magic in this world we can't explain.

shrug

Haih, as long as this "friend" doesn't disturb us, I don't care.

Oh, I gotta go now.

Bye, honey.

Bye, witchy! Don't get possessed!

33

Since you've been a ghost for ages, I thought it'd be fun to show you what all the kids like now.

What's that?

It's a tablet.

Like a smaller TV?

Oh, you know what a TV is!

Well, it's kinda like that, except you can ask this TV to do anything you like.

It's got games, movies, books, the internet...

The internet?

You'll love the internet!

old cartoons 🔍

You can find anything you want on it instantly.

All you gotta do is type in your requests in this box here...

And VOILÀ! magic!

WOW!

Hey! I know this! I saw it once in the movies.

Ah, for real? This cartoon is from the seventies!

You gotta tell me what life was like back then!

Was it all in fuzzy color?

Why did everyone speak and dress funny?

I actually... don't remember much from my life.

Really?

I can recall pieces, like my name, and things can be familiar.

But I can't bring up memories on my own.

It's mostly a blur.

Weird.

Yeah, I've no idea why...

Here, lemme show you.

Oh! It's Halloween!

Yeah!

It's my favorite holiday!

How do you see the other stuff in this tablet?

09:30
Oct 31

It's got spooks and candy and all the things I love!

Like trick or treat!

Ohmigosh, Alexa! You gotta join me for trick or treat tonight!

How?

I'm a ghost.

Psh! We'll make it work.

But what about your, erm... non-ghost friends?

Nah, they aren't coming.

Why?

They are too old for stuff like this. The cool thing now is to go to the big kids' Halloween parties.

You weren't invited?

... I'm not going.

messages
carol
Party at 8!

Carol
Hey Lora, u coming?

Lora
Got plans. Sorry!!!

Oh...

because you already had one for your birthday, right?

36

Ma, I'm heading out now!

For trick or treat?

Yeah!

Don't come home late. 9 pm max.

Got it!

Whee!

Oh!

It's a small party. Just me hanging out with some high school buds. No pressure, though.

Erm... oh gosh, the big kids? I don't know...

Can you give us a sec?

She's your friend, right?

It's gonna be fine.

Besides, this is your chance to see what a real big kids' Halloween party is like!

Sigh. I know, but... I'm nervous.

Will you come with me?

Only if you go.

Alrighty!

We're partying.

Awesome! C'mon in!

Lemme tell my ma that I'm here first.

44

Hey, gals!

We've got guests! Everyone, meet Lora and Alexa!

Hey!

AWW, I love your costumes!

AYA

EMILY

OH-EM-GEE, are you a sheet ghost? I LOVE IT!!

HIYA

Way cuter than the trashy costumes they sell in stores.

Ha! You mean like—

Ms. Sexy Sea Cucumber.

Seductive anxiety.

The Male Gaze.

snorts

You nerds. There are babies in this room now, so you three better behave.

You hear?

Yes, Ms. Prissy.

We'll be on our BEST behavior.

hehe

hehe

I knew this would happen.

What would?

Sigh. That I'd be left out.

I mean... look at them. They are having fun talking...

And I can't keep up.

Why not? Aren't they friendly?

No! Yeah, I mean, just...

Sigh.

It's the same issue with the kids in school too...

They talk about celebs and memes and all kinds of stuff —

But the topics change so fast every day and...

I fall behind.

I stop talking.

Sometimes I wonder if people are pretending to still talk to me so they don't hurt my feelings...

49

That's why I don't like going to parties.

They remind me of how boring I am...

Lora. I've only been with you since yesterday.

But I know you're someone with tons of interesting things to say.

You like to read, right?

Yeah, and...?

Talk about that!

But it's all weird stuff!

Like the Bermuda Triangle and Bigfoot and...

It doesn't matter!

I know nothing about that stuff!

But I'd love if you would tell me more!

And I'm sure they will feel the same!

It's not "cool," though...

LORA! Don't let that make you afraid to be who you are.

If they don't jive with that, SO WHAT?

Your real friends don't love you for how "cool" you are —

They love you. For you.

CLICK

?

It's the night of nights, when we gather round for one very special event —

Lora, Alexa! Join us!

yay!

GHOST STORY NIGHT

Woot!

Yeah!

So, when I was nine, in my old school, I had to go pee, real bad.

The hallway to the toilet was so empty, and so quiet...

And the toilet itself was like that too. No one was in there, and despite it being well-lit, there were dark shadows inside the cubicles...

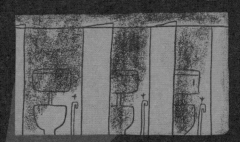

Ohh, nope.

After I was done, I went to wash my hands.

There was this long wall mirror above the sinks.

I looked up —

Saw myself...

... and her.

EXCUSE me? HER? What!

I thought she came in after me. Normal stuff.

Then I looked closer...

... and, gawd, I knew it instantly.

She wasn't anyone I knew in school.

Not anyone alive.

She was standing there staring at me, like —

"Dude, why did you wake me with your flushing?"

At this point, I had given up and just RAN the heck outta there!

aaahhhhh

LORD! You're lucky she wasn't mad!

Right?

Thing is, I'm still not sure she's real.

I mean, no joke, the toilet was super spooky!

Yiiikes!!

Here, your turn now.

Huh?

Er... I...I don't have a ghost story...

Not my own anyway. But I read in a book—

About this one house in Spain fifty-ish years ago—

where a family first discovered on their concrete kitchen floor...

FACES!

Or, well, images of faces that come and go for no reason over a span of twenty years...

55

Hmm, my bathroom has a big mirror. Let's do it!

WHAT?! You nuts? After YOUR story?

Aya, do you believe in ghosts?

NO. I mean, I don't know!

Then you've nothing to be afraid of!

Besides, what's the worst that could happen?

Maybe you'll see that sophomore Greg Koh's face in the mirror~

he he

Urgh, seriously, Sunni! You're gonna get us in real bad trouble someday!

Aw, chill, Aya. We don't live in a horror movie.

Lora, Alexa! C'mon!

58

Chapter 3:
Bloody mary

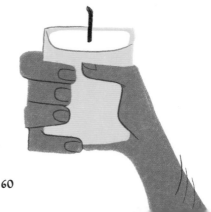

You know you can't bring your phone in there, right?

Candlelight only.

WHAT?
So you're telling me —

I gotta memorize all of this info?!

It's not that hard, is it? All you gotta do is . . .

Stand in front of a mirror, look into it,

 ←

and chant "Bloody Mary" three times.

Still!

You can't just do ghost things until you are, like, super sure —

Like, OMG —

What if you summon a demon?

flit

Thanks for bringing up Bloody Mary.

I was running out of party ideas.

Have you always liked spooky stuff?

Yeah.

Just that I never talked about it with anyone, 'cause it's... weird?

Are you kidding!

I'm into it too, like big-time!

Really?

Yeah! There's a huge community of spooky geeks online too.

I usually get my content from listening to podcasts.

Huh? Podcasts?

You've no idea what those are?

shakes head

Oh gosh! You're missing out!

You're in for a treat, Lora! Sunni knows the coolest stuff!

SLAM!

Oof! lemme in!

Hey!

OKIO-DOKIO!

I'm ready!

Lord help me...

Let's. meet. A GHOST.

Bloody Mary.

Bloody Mary.

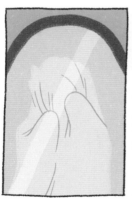

Bloody Mary!

Haha! Guess it didn't work! Let's go*oooo*! Wait—

AAAAHH AAAAAAAAH AAAH

Run! Run! Run!

OW!

Geez, your big butt!

Alexa?

hehe

Good news, everyone!

According to SCIENCE—

wiki page

Dim lights can trigger the mind to hallucinate.

That, plus fear, is what made us see Bloody Mary!

URGH, Em!

Why do you have to be such a nerd?!

kekeke~

But that's why I'm fun at parties.

Well, real or not, I ain't sleeping with the lights off tonight.

Hard agree.

nods

Wait, you're having a sleepover?

Yeah!

Oh no! It's almost nine o'clock.

We have to go now.

Awww.

We liked having you here. ♥

Thanks for coming to my party!

We had a blast.

Oh, oh! You should totally join us for the next sleepover!

Oh wow! Really?

Yeah! I just need your number.

Oh, wait, are we trading phone numbers now?

Hey, I want yours too!

Me three!

BOO!

WHOA!

Hehe, I didn't know ghosts can get spooked.

Well, now you know.

Whatcha reading?

Oh.

I picked up a magazine in your friend's room earlier.

I was curious.

Teen Power. Fashion trends for the more stylish you.

Don't miss J-Monáe's... This new meme is taking over...

Ehhh.

You really like using that tablet, huh?

Yeah!

I think it's far out.

It really knows how to find anything.

No regrets going to a big kids' party, hmm?

...
Nope.

Sunni

Thanks for making me go.

yawn

And for helping out.

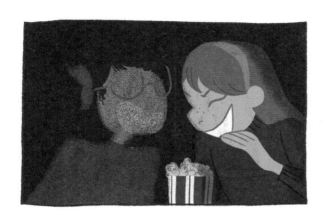

Huh?

What for?

Oh, why did you bring it along, then?

Well...

It's 'cause I wanted to be a witch's apprentice today.

I like dressing up as whatever I wanna play as.

It makes it feel more real to me.

Rad! Do you have a story for your apprentice?

Hmm. Lemme think...

10K

86

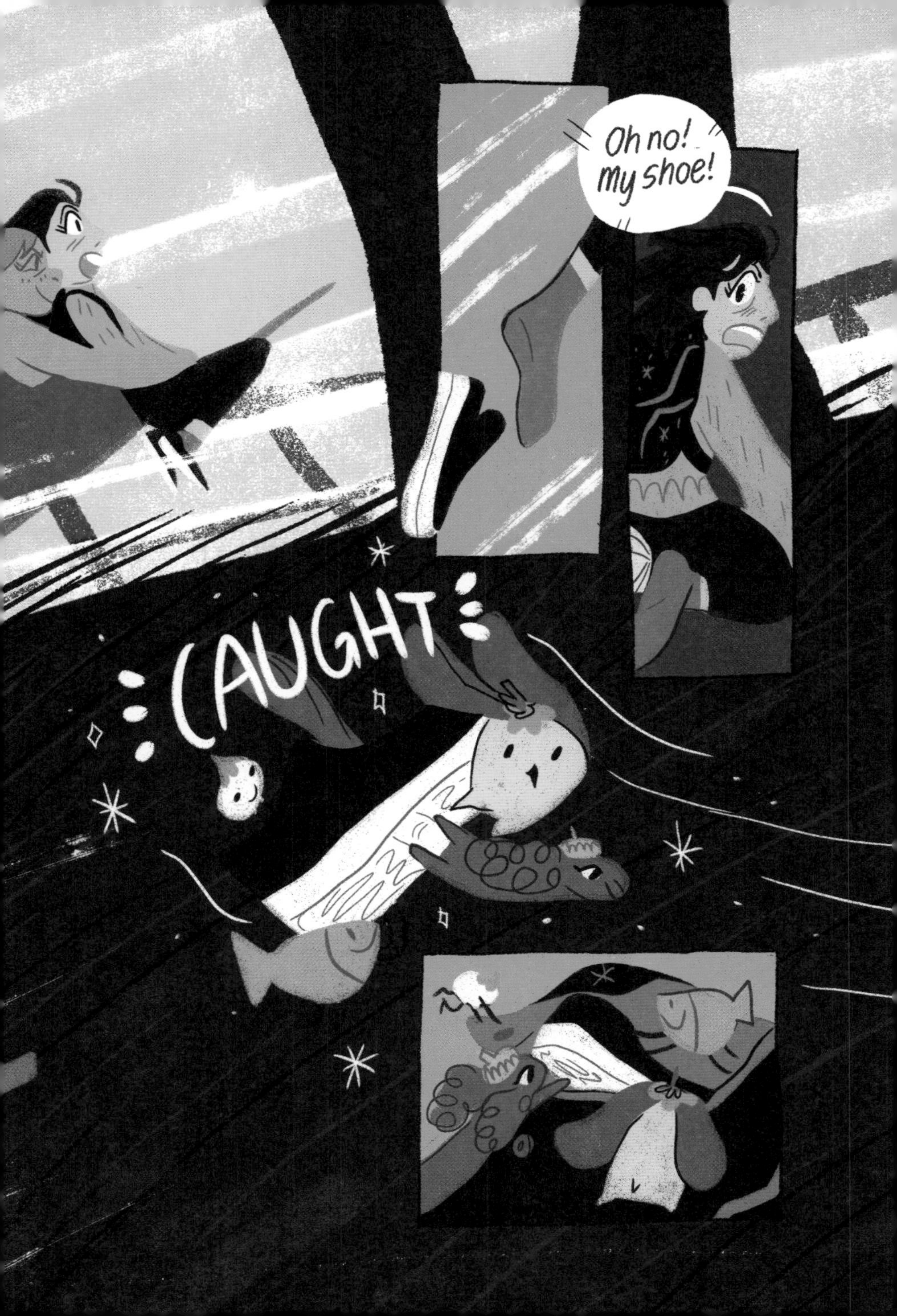
Oh no! my shoe!
CAUGHT

ah!

POP

I missed coming here.

You haven't been?

Not really.

You saw how much work it took getting up here.

It wasn't fun going up alone.

So I stopped.

None of your friends wanted to join you?

Did I say something wrong?

You can be a kid for as long as you like.
It'll be okay,
because I'll be here to keep this magic with you.
We'll have each other, always.

Chapter 5:
Old Friends

Hmm, this place...

It all feels so familiar.

Maybe you studied here before?

Maybe.

Yeah.

If I did study here, it sure looks fancy now.

Uh-huh.

Oh, hey, you wanna come along with me to class?

...Nah. I'll pass.

I wanna tour the school.

See what's changed.

Cool, okay!

See ya after school!

1976

LINE ENTRY

Hey.

...Hey.

Happy belated birthday.

Seriously?

Yeah, I . . . gah.

I'm sorry, Lo.

It's not like I forgot.

Just that . . .

There was a lot that went down last weekend.

Was that why you weren't here on Friday?

. . . Yeah.

I'm sorry —

for ignoring your texts, and not being there for your birthday.

You got me a gift, though?

No, Lo. It's more serious than that.

Sigh. I fell out with some guys who I thought cared about me...

The things they joke about... I couldn't stand their toxicity anymore.

Real friends don't abandon you after you stop being "cool" to them. We all got to have each other's back, you get me?

And I realized that was what I didn't do for you.

Urgh. Man, I'm such a jerk.

...

Look.

If you don't want to talk to me anymore, I getchu. We're cool.

I only wanted to let you know I messed up.

I'm sorry. I hope I'll earn your forgiveness one day.

Hmm, I accept your apology.

Tentatively.

Whew.

Thanks, bro.

You gotta do more than just giving me cat ears, though.

Haha! Of course, as you wish.

BRINNNGG

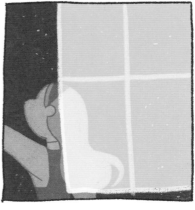

I climbed the monkey bars today.

Did you? Bueno!

Abuelita!

My new friend Alexa helped me — she has flying powers!

Haha!

That is very handy!

You know. . .

I used to have a friend called Alexa too.

Diana?

WHOA!

rustle

Chapter 6:
Part I: Growing Up

Sunni

Omg this is so you!!!

When you want to be goth and preppy

Lora

hahaha really?

Bobby
 Hey bro, wanna hang Fri?

Lora
 Totes!

——————— Fri ———————

Lora
 Thanks for letting me play Chef Chaos. So fun!

Bobby
 IKR. It's wild!

Lora
 I wanna play again!

127

Sunni
did you finish the podcast yet??

what do you think? :)

Lora
I'm only halfway but OMGGG so spooky! I love it!

Emily
RIP @ me. Rly gotta find time to listen to it

Darn it, exams!! FREE ME

Lora
Haha oh yeah, I'm swamped too.

Lora

I know nothing about makeup.

Emily

lol same

I'm curious to see how I'd look with it tho . . .

Sunni

emi, let's!!!!

find out, I mean.

oh you too, Lora!

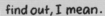

Aya

MALL TRIP

Hiya

M A L L T R I P

Emily

Lora

I've always seen the girls in cartoons wear dark lipstick and really liked it.

But it never occurred to me that I can do that in real life?

 I'm so glad it looks good. I feel like I'm more myself on the outside now.

Q that!

☀ sunniallday

—— couple of boba before watching #
—— lol was it as scary as they said?

Q that!

☀ sunniallday

—— SQUAD! #bffs
—— ♥ ✿ ♥
—— love yall <3

Q that!

☀ sunniallday

—— it's this lil goblin's bday! love to hate ya!! LOL
—— wow RUDE

How mad do you think the Student Club would be if I did?

Why don't you find out yourself?

keke

See ya.

SPRI PROM

TICKET

Chapter 6:
Part II : Growing Old

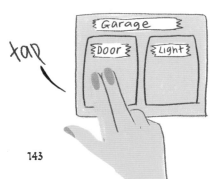

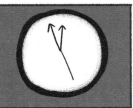

Da da da! whooshh

Hehe!

Mijo! Mama is here!

Si!

I'm going home with Mama now.

Are you coming?

No.

But I'll see you in school on Monday.

Okay!

Bye-bye, Alexa!

Bye-bye.

ding

National Writer's Award
presents
Diana Rodriguez
Lifetime Achievement Award

Writer weaves world with magic

Hello there.

Need anything?

Wh- I— erm...
aren't you afraid of me?

Afraid of you?
Haha!

What for?
I'm old—

I've seen many strange
things in my life.

Never imagined I'd have a
ghost as a houseguest, though.

What's your
name?

Alexa.

As in, my
grandson's
imaginary
friend, Alexa?

Yeah, and also...

your old friend
from school...

Alexandra
Hudson.

SNORT

You're joking?

NO, sorry.

Whew. All right. Bienbienbien.

Dios mío. I'm sorry.

It's a lot to take in.

I know.

You died when we were . . . what? Fourteen?

Was that how old I was?

Yes. It's been some fifty years. . .

Why did you come back?

I never left.

Then how am I able to see you now?

You just do, and . . . you didn't run away.

Kids don't run from me. They see me as their friend. But with grown-ups . . .

They don't look.

Heh. I always pride myself on being a child at heart.

Part of my craft.

Speaking of —

I make books for children.

To me, it's important to keep the mind and spirit young. Not just to make good stories —

The Fairies of Faring Forest

Diana Rodriguez

But also to live a good life.

155

This is the story of
a girl, one Alexa Hudson.

She was a sickly child.
Her illness made it hard
for her to be with other
children.

She stared out the
window every day, and
longed to run and
jump and play...

...just like
everyone else.

As she grew, she became well
enough to attend school.

For a while, she learned to make
friends, to laugh, and to blossom.

Sadly,
        it was not to last.

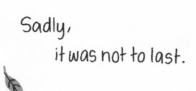

Before her fourteenth birthday,
        she fell ill once more.

        It caused her so much pain,
            she was forced to stay in bed.

Her parents sought help
from the best doctors.
Her friends tried to
restore her joy.

Nothing worked.

One day,

a special friend came to visit.

Come, they said. It is time to go home.

She took their hand.

And left for a different world, where she would never endure another day of pain and tears...

Or, at least —

That was what everyone thought.

Thank you, Diana. I...

I think I get it now.

For a long time, I couldn't remember who I was before I died . . .

But I must have forgotten on purpose at the start.

If I forget everything — the hurt, the sadness, and all the years I lost . . .

I can start over and stay a child forever.

That was all I ever wanted.

Chapter 6:
Part III: Growing Out

Cafe with Caroline

Nasrul's 1st championship

TO-DO

em ∅ Math
pg50-1
∘ set up art account??
∘ meeting with
student club
@ 3
oh yeah, talk to
B about
design

art.soul   800 fans
                            92 follows
dansemacabre
Lora X

BBQ
Art Club
End of Year

← Oaksfield Middle
Cemetery Road →

Oh!

Before I forget...

Come look.

These are some of the things that were precious to me as a child.

This toy camera, Mr. Bunny Bombom, a few love letters... Hehe!

Look at how cute we were.

bffs forever

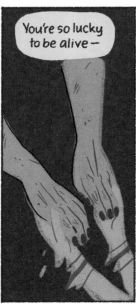

Cherish it.

Picking out clothes is WAY easier.

Should I go all black?

Too goth?

Or floral?

Hmm.

Maybe I should try going all out since this will be my first prom...

Then again—

Would it be worth the investment?

It's happening.

I am tired — Of watching everyone move on without me.

When is it my turn?

Look at her.

ding

She's all grown up.

And me?

I need to grow up too.

chapter 7:
Graveyard

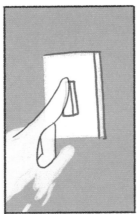

Darn!

I keep forgetting.

It's a lovely morning here in Oaksfield!

Enjoy it while you can...

As we'll be battered by a real beast of a thunderstorm this evening.

03

Expect a dreary rush hour, commuters.

And keep your feet dry!

Oh! Good morning, Alexa.

I didn't hear you ring.

...

You don't look happy.

What's wrong?

Diana, I...

I want to go.

Go? To where?

That's why.

Is there anything we can do?

No. It's my choice.

I can't keep being a ghost girl forever.

I hope you understand.

Alexa . . .

Sigh.

If that is your wish, then I must accept it.

Thank you.

But, please —

Is there anything I can do for you?

Well . . .

Could you walk with me around Oaksfield —

One last time?

B-bobby! You're still here?

Urgh, yeah. Sorry.

I just lost my last baby tooth. Look!

Ew, gross.

Yep, gross!

Au revoir, mr. Tooth!

But seriously, why were you yelling?

Haha!! I dunno! I just like keeping the ghost in my house company!

...

You're weird, you know that?

You used to talk with these characters you'd make up for us to play with.

Haha, those were good times.

Alexa,
please come out.

Allie?

She's gone.

Did I ...

push her

away?

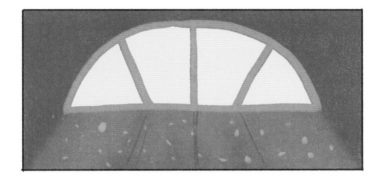

There must
be some way
I can find her.

History:

The Four Elements music
- - - - - - - - - - - - -

dachshund size
- - - - - - - - - - - - - -

how do you pronounce . . .
- - - - - - - - - - - - - -

Alexa Hudson 1977 obituary
- - - - - - - - - - - - -

Diana Rodriguez books
- - - - - - - - - - - - -

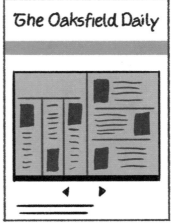

Alexandra Hudson, d. 18 Sept, 1977
Fallen Oaks Cemetery

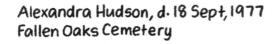

Buried at Fallen Oaks, huh?

How much time do I have?

Okay. Cool.

I got...

Three hours.

I can do this!

YEAH!

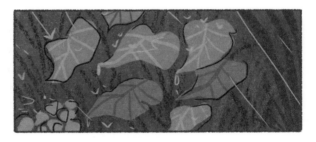

How will I
get out of
here?

URGH!

...

Am I gonna die here?

NO! No, no.

I won't die!

I'll find a way out somehow!

I won't be scared! It's okay. It's just—

breathes

It's just like being on an adventure.

Yeah! That's right!

I'm Lora Xi, world-famous explorer—

Currently inside the tomb...

...of an ancient storm god.
KRABOOM
My mission...
is to find my best friend, Alexa.

I'll escape this tomb.

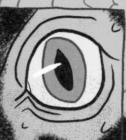

And I'll find her.

C'mon, beast.

Show me what you got.

Chapter 8:
The Magic Place

We're here.

Are you sure this is where you want to be dropped off?

Yes.

CAMP BUNLEY
🅿 PARKING

This hill has special meaning to me.

You've done so much for me today...

Thank you, Diana.

Especially for driving so slowly in the rain so I could keep up!

Ha ha!

It's all good!

I imagine it's not easy to sit in a car with an incorporeal body!

BBP BEEP BB BP or BP

...

It was lovely to reconnect.

Reliving our childhood days...

I don't even mind how brief it was.

me too.

I can't think of anyone better to spend my last day with.

chuckles

Best friends forever?

Best friends forever.

Oh, Alexa!

Will Lora be okay?

With you going?

Lora's at her first prom tonight. She will be with her friends . . .

If she's like any of the kids I used to play with—

She will be fine.

07:03PM

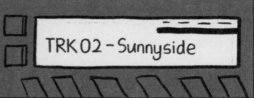

TRK 02 - Sunnyside

BRAKE

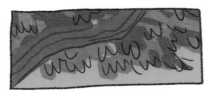

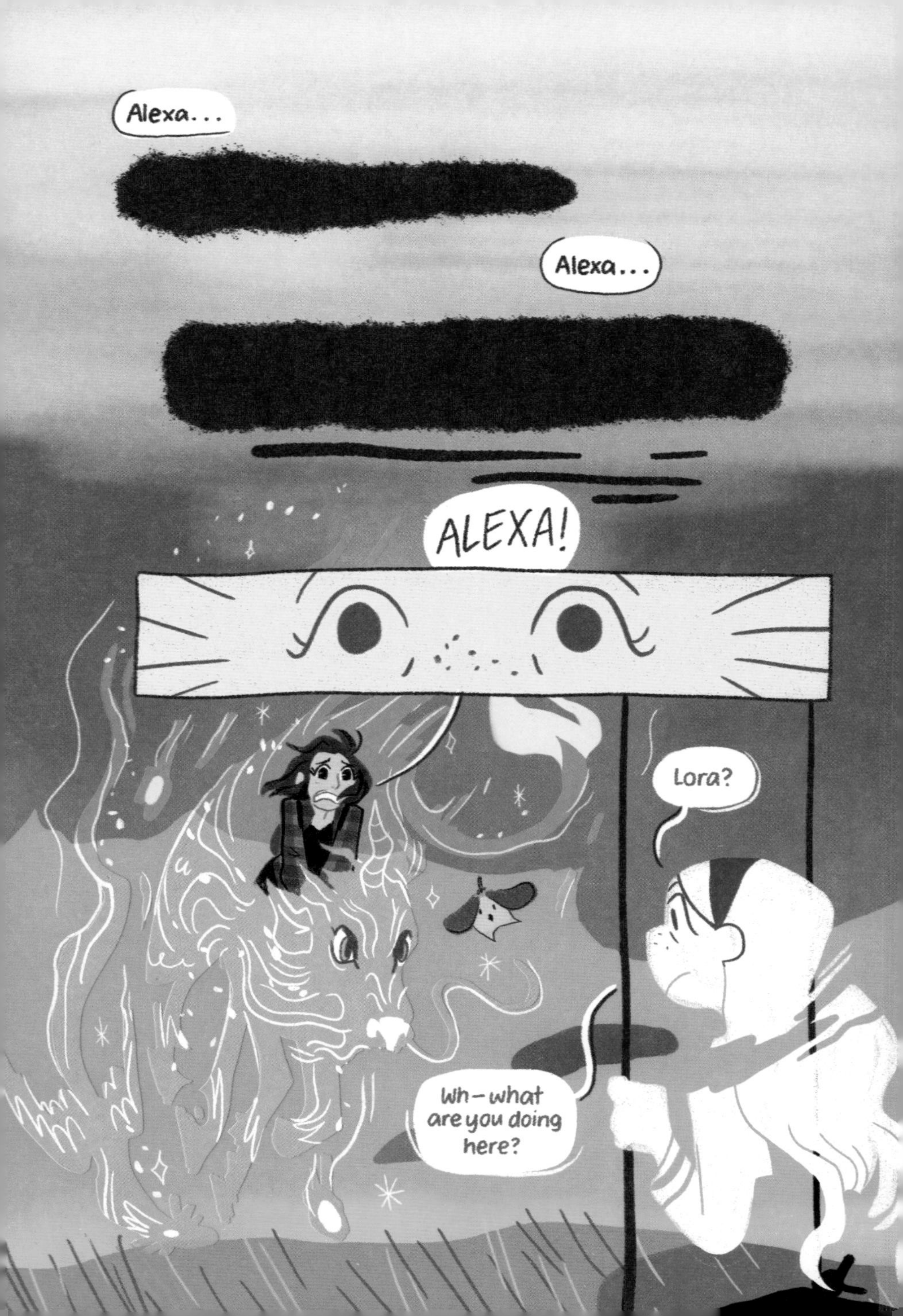
Alexa...
Alexa...
ALEXA!
Lora?
Wh-what are you doing here?

Fifty years ago,
I died from an illness.

I barely got to live
my childhood.

So when I came back,
I forgot my old life
and became an
imaginary friend
to all the kids who lived
in the house after me.

You'll be okay. You won't ever lose that magic.

You know why?

Because I'm not that magic.

You are.

You created that magic as a kid.

You'll create that magic as a grown-up.

And you'll still do it even when you're old and gray.

There is nothing to be scared of —

When you have a whole life to look forward to.

Sniff

And the best thing is, you won't be alone.

Really?

Really. I know.

This world is so big, and full of people who keep the magic in their lives.

When you see them — and you will — they will recognize you. Young or old.

And they will love you.

When I said you've grown up, what I meant was —

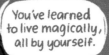

You've learned to live magically, all by yourself.

I don't want to be the one who holds you back.

And I need to move on and find my own life too.

Please, Lora, for the both of us —

Are you ready?

It's funny.

What is?

I planned to ask you to prom.

But then I had to goof up and sprain my ankle. And now I'm late.

Oh no!

It's okay.

I'm not upset about missing prom. There's always next year. Still...

It'd have been nice to go.

Y'know, We can still have our own prom here.

Shall we dance?

But I can't touch you, and my ankle...

Hehe, silly. We play pretend.

Now, c'mon—

Give me one last dance!

...

Sure. Let's.

Alexa.
You still
there. . .?

· · ·

Oh.
Sorry. I didn't
mean to. . .

I'll take my
leave —

Wait.

Alexa already
said goodbye.

She's finally
moved on. . .

We both
have.

OW!

What's
wrong?

epilogue

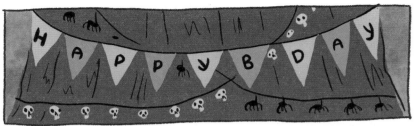

ALEXANDRA HUDSON

Sigh. Diana.

Do you miss her too?

ALEXANDRA HUDSON 1963 – 1977 Dearly beloved

Oh, yes, Lora.

Every day.

I keep thinking about what she told me before she left.

And I... I've no idea if I'm doing it right.

She said if I keep my magic, I'll find friends who get me.

Like you.

But I'm still scared.

How do I know if I'll be that adult she believed in?

What if I mess up?

I don't know, Diana.

Happy birthday.

bffs forever

Shall we make a toast?

Acknowledgments

I acknowledge that this book was written and illustrated in Melbourne, Australia, and published in New York City, USA—on which the Wurundjeri people of the Kulin Nation and the Lenni Lenape people are the Traditional Custodians of their respective land. I pay my respect to their Elders both past, present, and emerging, and extend that respect to other First Nation people of Australia and Native Americans of North America.

I would like to express my gratitude to the team at Random House Graphic: Gina Gagliano, publisher powerhouse; Whitney Leopard, editor extraordinaire; Patrick Crotty, designer wizard; and Nicole Valdez, marketing magician. Thank you so much for believing in me as an author. It was a joy to work with you all.

As usual, I want to shower my agent Jen Linnan with a thousand and one biodegradable confetti, each spelling out "thanks!!" and "you're the best ♥♥♥"

I wish to send a shout-out to my friends and family who supported me during the making of *Séance Tea Party*, especially Nastasia, Alison, Kite, and Taylor for being my first readers.

Finally, thank you, reader, for picking up this book.

Reimena Yee is a strange and fancy illustrator, writer, and graphic novelist. Hailing from the dusty city of Kuala Lumpur, Malaysia, she originally studied STEM before pursuing her passion for the world and all of its histories and cultures.

She is the author-illustrator of the historical gothic fantasy *The Carpet Merchant of Konstantiniyya*, the first Malaysian graphic novel to be nominated for an Eisner Award. She is also the writer for the Makers Club series.

She has illustrated for multiple clients including Girls Make Games, the Adventure Time comics, Random House Children's Books, and Hasbro.

In addition, she is the cofounder of UNNAMED, a comics collective network created to build community and resources for visual-literary creators in Southeast Asia, through panels, workshops, and public outreach.

🐦 @reimenayee
📷 @reimenayee
reimenayee.com • blog.reimenayee.com

Early character drawings and notes on Alexa and Lora. I drew these when I first told my publisher I wanted to make a book about them!

- 12 years old
- quiet, lonely
- likes cryptids, weird phenomena, mythology.

Lora Zi

Alexa
- dead since the 60's
- 13 years old convent school gal
- curious, fun.

The original artwork that inspired the story.
Drawn in 2016, done for fun!

After a few tries (at both drawing and writing), I ended up with a cast of three (and a half) main characters. These were their final designs.

The other characters came as the story developed.

Sunni was called a different name then.

Lucky

Batrisha

Mrs. Xi

Mr. Xi

Hira

Priya

Emily

Bobby

Aya

My book designer, Patrick, and I tossed around some ideas for the cover. First, he gave me his sketches.

Then I drew my own sketches based on a few of Patrick's ideas I really liked.

We chose this one!

From sketch . . .

. . . to nearly finished!

Patrick made this very pretty
text design for the title
(better than mine, haha).

What you see on the front
cover is a collaborative
process with lots of talking
and drawing involved.

Here's how I make comics.

I do an OUTLINE. I get the basic idea of how I want to tell a story and a character's journey, from start to end.

Then I spend a long time THINKING, aka DOING OTHER THINGS. During this time, the story will grow, change, get new ideas, lose old ones, and so on. I don't force my creativity, and I let my story ideas come to me whenever they want.

Once I have thought enough, I write a BIGGER OUTLINE. Then I get to writing the SCRIPT. This is what my script looks like.

I write using dialogue with minimal narrative direction, and little to no notes on the artwork. My focus when I write a script is on the story and characters. If both are strong, the art follows easily (for me anyway).

> While she talks, she flips through the pages of the chapter: the White Lady, Bloody Mary, Will-o-Wisps, and seances...
>
> Lora: Hmm...feeling an idea coming...(snaps fingers) Let's hold a seance!
>
> She turns to her toys.
>
> Lora: Not just a seance – a seance tea party! Whee-hee! (picks up her cat and bat plush) C'mon!
>
> She brings up a tea set to the attic, as well as some birthday cake and a crystal ball. She makes an (inaccurate) ouija board and planchette out of cardboard and markers.
>
> Arrange herself and her toys/fairies (guests) around a circle, she begins her seance, raising her toy wand.
>
> Lora: Bada-*zing*!
>
> Nothing.

When my editor, Whitney, gives me the green light for the script, I move on to actually drawing the comic.

THUMBNAILS are little sketches of what I want a comic's page to look like. This is where I figure out where to place my characters, speech bubbles, and panels, and how all of those form an overall artistic composition. But they aren't the clearest. Compare these thumbnails with the final drawings. A big difference!

Afterward, I develop my thumbnails . . . sketches that look more like the final artwork. When I'm happy, I move on to . . .

THE ACTUAL DRAWING AND COLORING!

These are the two brushes I use in Photoshop.

Because of the art style of this book, I start by outlining the panel boxes, then FLATTING with various shades of black and gray to distinguish between characters, foreground objects, and backgrounds. Once I get the silhouettes done, I put in the real colors and details.

MAGIC, FANTASY, AND WONDER— ALL IN A GRAPHIC NOVEL

Aster and the Accidental Magic
by Thom Pico and Karensac

After a trickster spirit gives Aster three wishes, her new home suddenly gets interesting!

Kerry and the Knight of the Forest
by Andi Watson

There's a deep, dark forest on Kerry's way home. Will he find his way through or be trapped there forever?

Séance Tea Party
by Reimena Yee

Lora doesn't want to grow up—can her new ghost-friend, Alexa, change her mind?

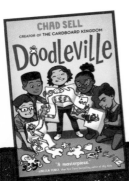

Doodleville
by Chad Sell

Drew's art is getting out of control . . . and escaping off the page!

Witches of Brooklyn
by Sophie Escabasse

Life in Brooklyn takes a strange turn when Effie discovers MAGIC runs in the family. . . .

5 Worlds
by Mark Siegel, Alexis Siegel, Xanthe Bouma, Matt Rockefeller, and Boya Sun

The Five Worlds are in danger. Can three unlikely heroes come together to save everyone?

VISIT US AT RHKIDSGRAPHIC.COM